# The STORY KEEPERS

Episode 7

# Roar in the Night

Brian Brown and Andrew Melrose

Ꞁ
CASSELL

**Cassell**
Wellington House, 125 Strand,
London WC2R 0BB

© Brian Brown and
Andrew Melrose, 1997

**Videos distributed by
S.P. Trust**
Triangle Business Park,
Wendover Road, Stoke
Mandeville, Nr. Aylesbury,
Bucks HP22 5BL
Tel. 01296 614430
Fax. 01296 614450

Designed by
Tony Cantale Graphics

First published 1997

**British Library Cataloguing-
in-Publication Data**
A catalogue record for this
book is available from the
British Library.

ISBN 0-304-33667-X

Printed in Italy by
Conti Tipocolor

Long ago, in the city of Rome, there lived a mighty ruler. His name was Nero. He thought he was a god, but the Christians knew he wasn't. So Nero hated them.

One day there was a great fire. Nero said the Christians started it, and he sent his cruel soldiers after them.

Marcus, Justin and Anna lost their parents during the fire. Ben the baker and his wife, Helena, took them into their home. There, in a time of great danger, they told the children stories about Jesus.

This book is about the adventures of the Storykeepers.

It was a stormy night. Inside the bakery,
Ben and Helena were tucking the children
in bed.
"Justin, do you think it is raining where
mother and dad are?" asked Marcus.
"Don't worry," said Ben. "We'll find them
one day."

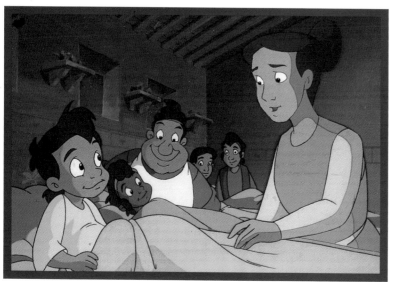

"We'll keep on looking for them," said Helena. "Just like the shepherd that Jesus told a story about."

A shepherd had a hundred sheep. He discovered one of them was missing.

He looked everywhere. Behind trees. Under rocks. In the bushes. He kept looking.

When he found the sheep he was so happy.
He carried the sheep back to his farm on his shoulders.
His friends were happy for him. They had a wonderful party because he had found his sheep.

Next day, Marcus wanted to play "find the lost sheep." "I'm helping Ben," said Justin. "We are making icing," said Anna. So Marcus played with Thastus, the goat.

Marcus heard a noise.
"Aachoo!"
He looked around
and saw two lion
cubs in the hay.
They had escaped
from a ship in the port.
But Marcus did not
know this.

Marcus thought the cubs were kittens. He gave them milk. They played with the hens and the other animals. What a noise they made! Helena came to see what was going on.
"I was only playing hide and seek with my kittens," Marcus told Helena.

"Can we keep them, please?" Marcus
asked Ben and Helena.
"Just for a while," said Ben.
Marcus was pleased. "I'll look after you,"
he told the cubs.
Zak was angry. He knew that the kittens
were lion cubs. Grown-up lions ate
Christians in the arena.

Ben went to see his friend Amicus, who owned a circus. "Have you lost two lion cubs?" Justin asked him. "They belong to the Emperor Nero," replied Amicus. He had an idea. He sent Ben to Saleem, the captain of a ship in the port.

Saleem and his family were Christians.
Ben asked Saleem to take the cubs back to
their home in Africa.
But Ben had no money to pay Saleem.
So Ben told a story instead.

Everywhere Jesus went crowds came to see him. Children, people who could not walk, sick people. They all wanted to touch him.

One day, some people brought a man who could not hear or speak.

Jesus took the man away by himself. He put his finger in his ears, spat, and touched his tongue. Jesus looked up and said: "Be opened!"

The man began to speak. And he could hear! Jesus told the man and his friends not to tell anyone.

"But I am going to tell everyone this story when I get back home in Africa," said Saleem.

Ben told Marcus that Saleem would
take the cubs.
"They will be safe in Africa," said
Ben.
Marcus was sad. But he knew it was
for the best. "I'm going to miss you,"
he said to the cubs.

Meanwhile, the lion trainer was angry. "Find those cubs!" he ordered his men. They took a pack of dogs and searched from house to house until they reached the bakery.

There was a knock on the door.
"It's Amicus. I'll open the door,"
said Ben.
The gang was shocked – it was the
lion trainer!
The men and the dogs rushed into
the bakery. They seized the cubs
and took them off in a cart.

"We've got to rescue them," said Marcus.
"They have their mother as well," said Amicus.
"We must save her too."
"We will need your cage and wagon," said Ben.

Ben, Amicus, Zak, and the children drove
in secret to the lion trainer's camp.
The children found a giant elephant horn
in Amicus's wagon. They set it up on the
hill above the training camp. Zak blew it by
mistake! It frightened an
elephant in the camp. The
elephant bellowed and
pulled at his chain.

All the guards rushed to see what was happening.
The lion cages were left unguarded. Amicus crept to the cages and opened the doors.
"Leo. Theo!" called Marcus to the two lion cubs.

"Call for your mother!" said Marcus to the cubs.
"Meow!"
"Meow!" The mother lion heard the cries. She leapt from her cage on to the wagon. Amicus drove off as fast as he could.

Down the bumpy road to the dockside
went the wagon. Dogs and more guards
chased after them.
"Here they come," Captain Saleem
shouted to his men. "Prepare to cast off!"

It was too late. Before they could get the lions and their cages on board, the guards arrived.

"Take them!" the trainer ordered. He knocked Amicus to the ground.

Ben and Helena stopped to help their friend. They thought that they would be captured. But suddenly Mangler, Amicus's oldest lion, saw them. He roared. "Man eater!" the guards shouted. They all ran away.

Amicus laughed. Mangler was his friend.

Amicus put his arms
around Mangler's neck.
"Good work, Mangler,
my old friend!" he said.
The sailors lifted the
cages on board.

"Good-bye," said Marcus to the cubs.
"You found your family after all. Maybe
someday I'll find my parents too."

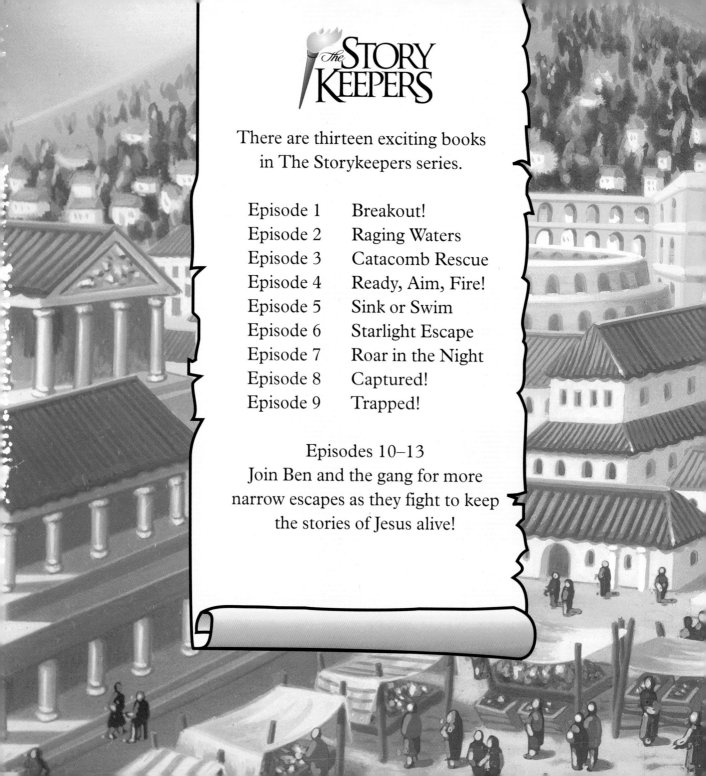

# THE STORY KEEPERS

There are thirteen exciting books
in The Storykeepers series.

Episodes 10–13
Join Ben and the gang for more
narrow escapes as they fight to keep
the stories of Jesus alive!